table of contents

A WORD FROM
CHIP INGRAM

God hard-wired into our DNA a need to belong, to be connected, to be loved and give love. That's why after God made Adam that He said that it was not good for Adam to be alone. So, He created Eve and the love story began.

Marriage is a wonderful gift from God and provides us an opportunity to share the journey of life with another person. When we stand and exchange our vows and pledge our love we have such high hopes and dreams. But, marriage is hard and often those dreams turn to nightmares.

Hope gets replaced with hurt. Passion is exchanged for pain. And, romance turns to resentment. Fifty percent of all couples who sign a marriage license will eventually choose to opt out and walk away rather than live with the pain and frustration any longer.

Here's the good news. Marriage doesn't have to end in disappointment. It really, actually can be a love story with a happy ending. And, God, the designer and architect has given us a blueprint to follow.

During this series we are going to explore God's design for marriage. More than simply understanding God's pattern for marriage, I want you to experience God's best for your marriage. It will not be easy. It will take focus and hard work and unselfishness. But the payoff is huge.

These sessions will be practical, fun, and challenging. You are going to learn things about yourself and your spouse that you never knew. You are going to acquire some tools that will strengthen your marriage.

Learning to love a person for a lifetime is one of the hardest and yet most rewarding things you will ever do. So, let's roll up our sleeves and get to work.

Teaching Pastor, Living on the Edge

EXPERIENCING
GOD'S DREAM
FOR YOUR MARRIAGE

Experiencing God's Dream for Your Marriage

HOW TO GET THE MOST OUT OF THIS EXPERIENCE

You and your spouse are about to begin what could be a life-changing journey for your marriage. This powerful marriage series taught by Chip Ingram provides some breakthrough teaching about developing a healthy marriage according to God's design. Listed below are the segments you will experience each week as well as some hints for getting the most out of this experience. If you are leading the group, you will find some additional help and coaching on pages 78-96.

TAKE IT IN

During this section you will watch the video teaching. Chip will introduce each session with a personal word to the group. Then, you will watch the teaching portion of the video. At the end of the teaching segment, Chip will wrap up the session and help the group dive into discussion.

A teaching outline with fill-ins is provided for each session. As you follow along, write down questions or insights that you can share during the discussion time.

Even though most of the verses will appear on the screen and in your notes, it is a great idea to bring your own Bible each week. It will allow you to make notes in your own Bible and find other passages that might be relevant to that week's study.

TALK IT OVER

Several discussion questions are provided for your group to further engage the teaching content. Keep the following guidelines in mind for having a healthy group discussion.

- **Be involved.** Jump in and share your thoughts. Your ideas are important, and you have a perspective that is unique and can benefit the other group members.

- **Be a good listener.** Value what others are sharing. Seek to really understand the perspective of others in your group and don't be afraid to ask follow up questions.

- **Be Courteous.** Always treat your spouse and others in the group with utmost respect. When there is disagreement, focus on the issue and never turn the discussion into a personal attack.

- **Be focused.** Stay on topic. Help the group explore the subject at hand, and try to save unrelated questions or stories for afterwards.

- **Be careful not to dominate.** Be aware of the amount of talking you are doing in proportion to the rest of the group, and make space for others to speak.

- **Be a learner.** Stay sensitive to what God might be wanting to teach you through the lesson, as well as through what others have to say. Focus more on issues you need to work on rather than issues you think your spouse needs to work on.

LIVE IT OUT

These simple suggestions help the lesson come to life. Don't ignore them; give them a try! Most of these weekly assignments involve you and your spouse setting aside time for further discussion from that week's session. These heart to heart discussions could provide a significant breakthrough that could take your marriage to a whole new level. Check in with other couples during the week to encourage and challenge one another to follow through with these assignments.

GOD'S PROCESS

For this reason a man shall leave his father and his mother, and shall be joined to his wife; and they shall become one flesh.

— *Genesis 2:24 (NASB)*

Marriage Defined – it is a volitional, legal, public and spiritual commitment to another person.

1. "A man shall leave his father and mother" — *The Break*

Our response to our parents is to be independent.

The key = emotional and financial detachment

 TALK IT OVER

1. What were the one or two things that most attracted you to your mate?

2. Share one of your favorite memories of a time together with your mate BEFORE you got married.

GROUND RULES FOR DISCUSSION

- ▶ Focus on what you do have and build on it

- ▶ Make this a place for sharing honestly and safely

- ▶ Confidentiality is crucial

3. When you got married, how well did you do with the "leave and cleave" principle? What were some of the challenges to becoming independent of parents and others?

4. Chip said "The greatest thing you will ever do in your marriage is walk with God." How has your walk with God or at times your lack of walking with God impacted your marriage?

5. As you look back to the early years of your marriage, what kinds of issues surfaced that you didn't expect?

6. If you could sit down with a young couple who is getting married in a month, how would you complete the following statement… "If you want to have a great marriage, the best piece of advice I could give you is…"

 ## LIVE IT OUT

Set aside a half hour this week for focused, uninterrupted discussion with your spouse (no phones, computers, or TV).

Spend some time reminiscing about your dating, engagement and wedding. Here are some questions to "prime the pump".

► Re-live the story of how you first met or what you did on your first date or how you got engaged.

► What was your favorite "date" that you can remember with your spouse before you got married?

► What was something humorous that happened at your wedding or reception?

► What's the most meaningful memory of the days surrounding your wedding?

GOD'S DREAM
FOR YOUR MARRIAGE

PART TWO

During last week's session Chip finished by talking about "leaving and cleaving". Every healthy marriage moves from dependence on parents to interdependence on each other. But it is not enough to just "leave"; we must also learn what it means to "cleave" to our spouse. During this session we will continue to explore God's blueprint for marriage and how we move toward greater intimacy with our spouse.

 TAKE IT IN

GOD'S PROCESS...CONTINUED

1.   "A man shall leave his father and mother"—The Break (covered in the previous session)

2.   "Shall cleave to his wife"—The Bond

I recognize my need for my spouse.

3.   "Shall become one flesh" –The Blend

My allegiance and loyalty is to my spouse first.

Your marriage matters more than your kids.

Your marriage matters more than your job.

GOD'S REWARD

And the man and his wife were both naked and were not ashamed.

— *Genesis 2:25 (NASB)*

God's reward is intimacy.

INTIMACY TEST

On a scale of 1-5 (1 = strongly disagree, 5 = strongly agree), rate the following:

The greatest barrier to intimacy in marriage is insecurity.

Evidence of Spiritual Intimacy

_____ My spouse and I often tend to agree on many of the important issues concerning values and beliefs.

_____ We seem to practice honest confession followed by genuine forgiveness when one of us has hurt the other.

_____ As a couple, our spiritual closeness through prayer or sharing Scriptures insights is quite good.

Evidence of Emotional Intimacy

_____ I remember special times when my spouse and I shared strong emotions like grief, sadness, joy or brokenness.

_____ We seem to be good at giving one another undivided attention when listening or talking.

_____ Verbalizing my needs and desires concerning our relationship to my spouse would be normal for me.

Evidence of Physical Intimacy

_____ We seem to prioritize frequent times of quality talking and having dates to together.

_____ I'm comfortable communicating my sexual desires and preferences to my spouse.

_____ I'm very satisfied with my spouse's sensitivity in meeting my sexual needs.

GOD'S PURPOSE

1.   Physical reproduction and pleasure (Genesis 1:26-28; Proverbs 5:18-20).

2.   Relational Intimacy (Genesis 2:18, 25)

3.   Spiritual Impact (Ephesians 5:22-33)

 TALK IT OVER

Consider sub-grouping for the discussion time. By breaking into small groups (by couples) there will be more opportunity for people to share.

1.   What are the top 2 or 3 qualities that you like most about your mate?

2.   The Bible says that we are to "cleave" to our spouse. Chip said that our "allegiance and loyalty is to our spouse first". Over the years, what are some things that have gotten in the way of you putting your spouse first?

3.   The Bible says that in marriage husband and wife become "one flesh". Describe a time in your marriage when you felt especially close and connected to your spouse... when you felt as "one flesh".

4.   Developing spiritual intimacy is a challenge for most couples. Why do you think that is?

5.   What practical steps could you take to develop greater "spiritual" intimacy in your marriage?

6.   What practical steps could you take to develop greater "emotional" intimacy in your marriage?

 LIVE IT OUT

Set aside some time this week with your spouse to review the Intimacy Assessment you took during this week's session. Discuss ways that you could improve intimacy in your marriage.

WHAT WENT WRONG?
BARRIERS TO INTIMACY

PART ONE

Sincerity and love are not enough. Good people who genuinely love each other can still have a lot of problems and pain in their marriage. There are some very predictable barriers that most every couple faces. Some couples keep hitting the same barriers year after year. During this session Chip will help us not only identify the barriers, but learn how to move past them.

⊙ TAKE IT IN

A problem clearly defined is 50% solved.

Premise #1

We all have legitimate needs and *longings*.

Premise #2

God originally designed our spouse to be a *major tool* in His hands to meet those needs and longings.

Premise #3

The *"fall"* (sin, Genesis 3) short-circuited man's relationship with God, his mate, and his world.

Premise #4

What was once the most natural relational response (other-centered, grace-giving) is now the most unnatural of responses, requiring supernatural enablement and hard work to achieve.

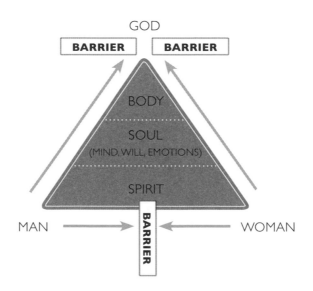

FOUR BARRIERS TO INTIMACY

1. _____ barrier = Sin, Shame, and Selfishness

> *Now the serpent was more crafty than any of the wild animals the LORD God had made. He said to the woman, "Did God really say, 'You must not eat from any tree in the garden'?"*

A Marriage Myth – **If you really love each other,** **it will all work out.**

> *The woman said to the serpent, "We may eat fruit from the trees in the garden, but God did say, 'You must not eat fruit from the tree that is in the middle of the garden, and you must not touch it, or you will die.'"*
>
> — *Genesis 3:1-3 (NIV)*

The first attack against mankind was an attack against God's word. The serpent said "you can't trust God's word".

The first theological error of mankind was to add to God's word. God never said Adam and Eve couldn't "touch" the fruit.

> *"You will not surely die," the serpent said to the woman. "For God knows that when you eat of it your eyes will be opened, and you will be like God, knowing good and evil." When the woman saw that the fruit of the tree was good for food and pleasing to the eye, and also desirable for gaining wisdom, she took some and ate it. She also gave some to her husband, who was with her, and he ate it.*
>
> — *Genesis 3:4-6 (NIV)*

The second attack is on God's character.

Satan – "God doesn't have your best in mind."

The same 3 things that tempted Adam and Eve and that tempted Jesus are the same 3 things that tempt us.

- ▸ She saw – lust of the eyes
- ▸ She took of the fruit and ate it – lust of the flesh
- ▸ It would make her wise – pride of life

> *Then the eyes of both of them were opened, and they realized they were naked; so they sewed fig leaves together and made coverings for themselves.*
>
> — *Genesis 3:7 (NIV)*

Adam and Eve's response to shame and hiding has been the response of mankind ever since.

Then the man and his wife heard the sound of the LORD God as he was walking in the garden in the cool of the day, and they hid from the LORD God among the trees of the garden. But the LORD God called to the man, "Where are you?" He answered, "I heard you in the garden, and I was afraid because I was naked; so I hid."

— Genesis 3:8-10 (NIV)

The average couple spends a lot of time hiding from each other.

And he said, "Who told you that you were naked? Have you eaten from the tree that I commanded you not to eat from?" The man said, "The woman you put here with me--she gave me some fruit from the tree, and I ate it." Then the LORD God said to the woman, "What is this you have done?" The woman said, "The serpent deceived me, and I ate."

So the LORD God said to the serpent, "Because you have done this, "Cursed are you above all the livestock and all the wild animals! You will crawl on your belly and you will eat dust all the days of your life. And I will put enmity between you and the woman, and between your offspring and hers; He will crush your head, and you will strike His heel."

To the woman he said, "I will greatly increase your pains in childbearing; with pain you will give birth to children. Your desire will be for your husband, and he will rule over you."

— Genesis 3:11-16 (NIV)

God delivers three curses...
- ▶ **One on the Serpent**
- ▶ **One on the Woman**
- ▶ **One on the Man**

From this point on, life would have difficulty and pain attached to it. The pain and difficulty would help us to discover that we need God.

The LORD God made garments of skin for Adam and his wife and clothed them.

— Genesis 3:21 (NIV)

God sheds blood as a foreshadowing of Christ's sacrifice and then He covers their shame.

And the LORD God said, "The man has now become like one of us, knowing good and evil. He must not be allowed to reach out his hand and take also from the tree of life and eat, and live forever." So the LORD God banished him from the Garden of Eden to work the ground from which he had been taken. After he drove the man out, he placed on the east side of the Garden of Eden cherubim and a flaming sword flashing back and forth to guard the way to the tree of life.

— Genesis 3:22-24 (NIV)

Our marriages will always be hard because at our core we all struggle with selfishness.

The barrier is spiritual (sin, shame, and selfishness) and the answer is _____ .

TALK IT OVER

1. What new insight did you get from this teaching and what impact should it have on your marriage?

2. Before you got married, what were your dreams and expectations of what marriage would be like? What did you hope for?

3. In terms of your personality and how you relate to others, are you more "closed off" or "open and transparent"? How does this impact your marriage?

4. Chip said "The average couple spends a lot of time hiding from each other." In your opinion, why do couples "hide" from each other? Give some specific examples of times when this has been true in your marriage

5. Just like Satan attacked Adam and Eve, he attacks our marriages. What have been some of the major attacks on your marriage?

6. Chip talked about the fact that "grace" is the answer to overcoming spiritual barriers. In what ways could you show "grace" to your spouse?

 LIVE IT OUT

Set aside some time this week to talk about the barriers to intimacy. Discuss your answers to the following question – "How can I make this a 'safe' marriage for you?"

Take the challenge of memorizing Romans 12:10 together as a couple. Discuss the verse together, work on memorizing it together, review it together throughout the week … and most importantly, work at putting this verse into action.

Love each other with genuine affection, and take delight in honoring each other.

— *Romans 12:10 (NLT)*

WHAT WENT WRONG?
BARRIERS TO INTIMACY

PART TWO

Last session we began exploring barriers to intimacy, the first being "spiritual barriers". During this session Chip will identify 3 other barriers that impact every marriage. You will see more clearly some of the barriers that may have been frustrating your marriage for years. This session could be that breakthrough that allows your marriage to go to a whole new level of intimacy.

TAKE IT IN

4 BARRIERS TO INTIMACY – (CONTINUED)

**Let your differences be
a source of celebration
rather than irritation.**

1. **Spiritual barrier = Sin, Shame, Selfishness (covered in the previous session)**

2. **Psychological Barriers =** _____ **Differences**

    Example – Introvert vs. Extrovert

    The Answer = Understanding

3. **Gender Barriers = Male and Female Differences**

    The Answer = _____

4. **Historical Barriers = "Our baggage" from the** _____

    The Answer = Knowledge

MALES TEND TO BE...

▸ MORE ACHIEVEMENT FOCUSED

▸ MORE THEORETICAL AND GENERALIST

▸ MORE INFORMATION ORIENTED IN COMMUNICATION

▸ MORE ACTION ORIENTED

▸ MORE FACTS ORIENTED

▸ MORE GOAL ORIENTED

FEMALES TEND TO BE...

▸ MORE RELATIONALLY FOCUSED

▸ MORE SPECIFIC AND DETAIL ORIENTED

▸ MORE EMOTION ORIENTED IN COMMUNICATION

▸ MORE VERBAL ORIENTED

▸ MORE INTUITIVELY ORIENTED

▸ MORE SUPPORTIVE AND NURTURING ORIENTED

Taken from: To Understand Each Other by Paul Tournier

THE SUMMARY –

The Result – We knowingly and unknowingly put up "protective walls" that keep us from being deeply touched and loved in ways we are desperate to experience.

God desires you to be an agent of grace and healing in the life of your mate.

Women focus on _____, struggle with loneliness and fear of abandonment.

A woman's wrong strategy centers around controlling.

Men focus on _____, struggle with futility and fear of failure.

A man's wrong strategy centers around compensating.

God's solution – Honest, grace-filled, understanding and communication will lovingly "pull down" the walls, risk vulnerability and restore intimacy.

TALK IT OVER

1.   What new understanding did you get of your mate as you listened to this week's teaching?

2.   What three words or phrases would you use that would best describe your spouse's personality?

3.   Share a couple of ways in which your personality is different from your spouse's. What is one difference in your spouse that you have come to appreciate?

4.   Chip talked about Gender Barriers as one of the things that can hinder intimacy. Read over the chart again about male and female tendencies. How accurate is the chart in describing you? How accurate is the chart in describing your spouse? Is there any place where the chart is "off track" in describing you or your spouse?

5.   What have you learned about your spouse's background and past that has helped you better understand how to relate to them?

 LIVE IT OUT

Set aside some time this week to talk about your family history. These questions will help you get the conversation started.

▸   How would you describe your parent's marriage?

▸   What did your mom and dad do well in their marriage?

▸   What dysfunctional patterns did you observe in your family?

▸   What "emotional baggage" from your past did you bring into your marriage?

For Extra Credit…

Chip said we knowingly and unknowingly put up "protective walls" that keep others out. Ask your spouse this week "What are some ways that I unknowingly put up protective walls that end up hindering our relationship?"

# RESOURCES

▸ The Intimacy Factor by David and Jan Stoops

▸ His Needs, Her Needs by Willard F. Harley, Jr.

▸ How to Overcome the Pain in Your Past CD Series by Chip Ingram. Visit LivingontheEdge.org.

HOW TO
SHARE HEARTS
INSTEAD OF
EXCHANGE WORDS

PART ONE

There are few things more important to a great marriage than communication. Yet, at times it feels like we don't even speak the same language as our spouse. During this very practical session you will begin to learn how to communicate more clearly and effectively with your spouse — moving from shallow, surface communication to "heart" communication.

 TAKE IT IN

UNDERSTANDING THE COMMUNICATION PROCESS

Definition: The Meeting of _____

Communication is the highway upon which love travels.

"Communication is the privilege of exchanging vulnerabilities."

— *Norman Wright*

"Communication is the process of sharing yourself verbally and nonverbally in such a way that the other person can both accept and understand what you are saying."

— *Norman Wright*

THE COMPLETE MESSAGE

▸   Words Alone = _____ % of meaning

▸   Tone of Voice = _____ % of meaning

▸   Total Non-Verbal = _____ % of meaning (Facial Expressions, Gestures, Posture)

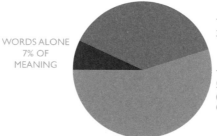

WORDS ALONE
7% OF
MEANING

TONE OF VOICE
38% OF MEANING

TOTAL NON-VERBAL
55% OF MEANING
(FACIAL EXPRESSIONS,
GESTURES, POSTURE)

FIVE LEVELS OF COMMUNICATION

LEVEL	TYPE	DESCRIPTION
LEVEL 1	CLICHÉ CONVERSATIONS	SAFE, SHALLOW, POLITE
LEVEL 2	REPORTING FACTS	REFERS BASICALLY TO THIRD PERSON
LEVEL 3	IDEAS OR JUDGMENTS	RISK BEGINS HERE (ATTACHMENT OF SELF WITH FACTS)
LEVEL 4	FEELINGS AND EMOTIONS	LAYING SELF ON THE LINE
LEVEL 5	OPEN COMMUNICATION	TOTAL HONESTY, "MUTUAL UNDERSTANDING", VULNERABILITY

Taken from Why Am I Afraid To Tell You Who I Am? By John Powell

FIVE PRINCIPLES THAT WILL TRANSFORM COMMUNICATION IN YOUR HOME

1. Be _____ – Speak the truth in love.

It is easy to speak the truth.

It is easy to speak in love.

It is difficult to speak the truth in love.

> **Shallow communication is safe but it doesn't lead to intimacy.**

But speaking the truth in love, we are to grow up in all aspects into Him who is the head, even Christ,

— *Ephesians 4:15 (NASB)*

Finish, then, with lying and tell your neighbor the truth. For we are not separate unites but intimately related to each other in Christ.

— *Ephesians 4:25 (Phillips)*

Application – Make direct requests.

 TALK IT OVER

1. How would you describe the communication patterns you observed in your family growing up?

2. What is one thing you have learned about effectively communicating with your spouse?

3. We all communicate in various ways… words, tone of voice, gestures, eye contact, active listening, and body language. In your opinion, which of these do you need to improve to communicate better with your spouse?

4. Chip talked about 5 Levels of Communication. Reflect on your communication with your spouse over the last 90 days. Put a mark below on each line to indicate how often you are communicating at Levels 3, 4 or 5. Share your assessment.

Level 3 – Ideas or Judgments

Never   Occasionally   Regularly

Level 4 – Feelings and Emotions

Never   Occasionally   Regularly

Level 5 – Open Communication

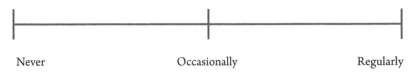

Never   Occasionally   Regularly

5.   What are some of the barriers that keep you and your spouse from communicating at a deeper, more intimate level? What are some practical steps that could help?

6.   Honestly assess yourself on the continuum below. Do you tend to communicate more on the "love" or "truth" side? Place a mark on the line below that reflects your natural bent.

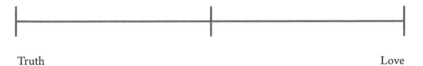

Truth   Love

 LIVE IT OUT

Make one direct request of your mate this week.

Set aside some time this week to discuss this session. Talk about the 5 levels of communication and how you can take your communication to a deeper level.

HOW TO SHARE HEARTS
INSTEAD OF
EXCHANGE WORDS

PART TWO

In every building project, it is important to have a set of blueprints. You've got to have a plan. But no building was ever built with just a set of blueprints. At some point, skilled workers must break out the tools and begin construction. During this session Chip is going to give us some very practical and helpful tools for communicating with our spouse.

 # TAKE IT IN

FIVE PRINCIPLES THAT WILL TRANSFORM COMMUNICATION IN YOUR HOME

1. Be *Honest* – Speak the truth in love. (covered in the previous session)

2. Be _____ – Deal with anger appropriately.

> *If you are angry, be sure that it is not out of wounded pride or bad temper. Never go to bed angry – never give the devil that sort of foothold.*
>
> — *Ephesians 4:26-27 (Phillips)*

Learn to use "I feel" messages.

The distance between your expectations and your experience is anger.

---

3. Be _____ – Work hard on your relationship.

> *If you used to be a thief you must not only give up stealing, but you must learn to make an honest living, so that you may be able to give to those in need.*
>
> — *Ephesians 4:28 (Phillips)*

4. Be _____ – Don't wound with your words.

> *Let there be no more foul language, but good words instead – words suitable for the occasion, which God can use to help other people. Never hurt the Holy Spirit. He is, remember, the personal pledge of your eventual full redemption. Let there be no more resentment, no more anger or temper, no more violent self-assertiveness, no more slander and no more malicious remarks.*
>
> — *Ephesians 4:29-31 (Phillips)*

5. Be _____ – Be the first to say, "I'm sorry."

> *Be kind to each other, be understanding. Be as ready to forgive others as God for Christ's sake has forgiven you.*
>
> — *Ephesians 4:32 (Phillips)*

What keeps us apart is pride.

PRACTICAL SKILLS AND SUGGESTIONS TO ENHANCE COMMUNICATION IN YOUR HOME

1. The Conference -- a Tool for _____

3 Questions

- ► What are you concerned about?
- ► What do you desire?
- ► What are you willing to do?

> **The relationship matters more than who is "right".**

2. Word Pictures – a Tool for _____

3. "Care" Lists – a Tool for *Building*

List 7 simple, loving, caring behaviors that are non-conflict producing and inexpensive that make you feel loved by your spouse.

To your spouse: I feel loved when you ...

1.

2.

3.

4.

5.

6.

7.

 TALK IT OVER

1. Split the group into couples. Arrange your chairs face to face and begin "the conference." Men, you go first. Ask your wife the following 3 questions. Then, ladies, you ask the same 3 questions of your husband.

    ▶   What are you concerned about?

    ▶   What do you desire?

    ▶   What are you willing to do?

    Remember, ask the question and then listen until your spouse is finished talking. When everyone has had adequate time, bring the group back together for the rest of the discussion time.

2. When are you most apt to wound with your words?

3. In your opinion, which of the 5 principles described in this session is the one that you and your spouse most need to work on?

4. Share one item on your Care List. "I feel loved when you…"

LIVE IT OUT

In the next 24-48 hours, set aside 1 hour to share your Care List with each other. Then, each day this week, take an item from your spouse's Care List and act on it.

Memorize another verse together this week. Hopefully you took the time to memorize Romans 12:10. Now, work on memorizing Ephesians 4:29, a great verse about communication. Work on this verse together as a couple.

Do not let any unwholesome talk come out of your mouths, but only what is helpful for building others up according to their needs, that it may benefit those who listen.

— Ephesians 4:29 (NIV)

THE FOUR KEYS TO
INTIMACY
PART ONE

It seems that many marriages in our generation are built on convenience and conditions rather than commitment. "I will stay with you as long as you meet my needs and as long as we are compatible and as long as this is still fun." No wonder so many marriages disintegrate. In this week's session, Chip will help us to see that before there can be intimacy, there must be the choice of unconditional commitment.

TAKE IT IN

1. THE "FUEL" OF _____ – A LIFELONG CHOICE OF UNCONDITIONAL LOVE TO AN IMPERFECT PERSON

No lasting change occurs until you put truth in practice.

> ▸ **The Mandate – Matthew 19:3-8**

So they are no longer two, but one. Therefore what God has joined together, let man not separate.
— Matthew 19:6 (NIV)

Take "divorce" off the table as an option for how you will solve your marriage problems.

> ▸ **The Rationale – To Love**

Our unconditional commitment of love to our spouse will help increase openness and vulnerability.

▶ **The How – A Weekly Choice**

> Love is like a muscle
> that gets built by
> constant exercise.

▶ **Challenge – Every day choose to do something you don't feel like doing that communicates love to your mate.**

… God has said, "Never will I leave you; never will I forsake you."

— *Hebrews 13:5b (NIV)*

 TALK IT OVER

1. Share one thing your mate did in this last week that made you feel like your mate is committed to you.

2. What are some of the messages in our culture that undermine a couple's LIFELONG commitment to each other?

3. As a group, make a list of negative consequences that can come when someone walks away from their marriage and chooses divorce?

4. Share a time when someone was committed to you and stood by you when life got really hard.

5. What couple do you respect because of their lifelong and unconditional commitment to each other? What have you observed in their relationship that inspires you?

6. Have a time of prayer. Pray for protection and commitment. Get a couple of chairs and set them in the middle of the circle. Then, couple by couple, let them sit in the chairs while the rest of the group lays hands on them and prays for them.

 LIVE IT OUT

Get out your care list this week and every day do just one thing that is on your spouse's list.

Write a love letter to your spouse declaring your LIFE LONG commitment.

THE FOUR KEYS TO
INTIMACY

PART TWO

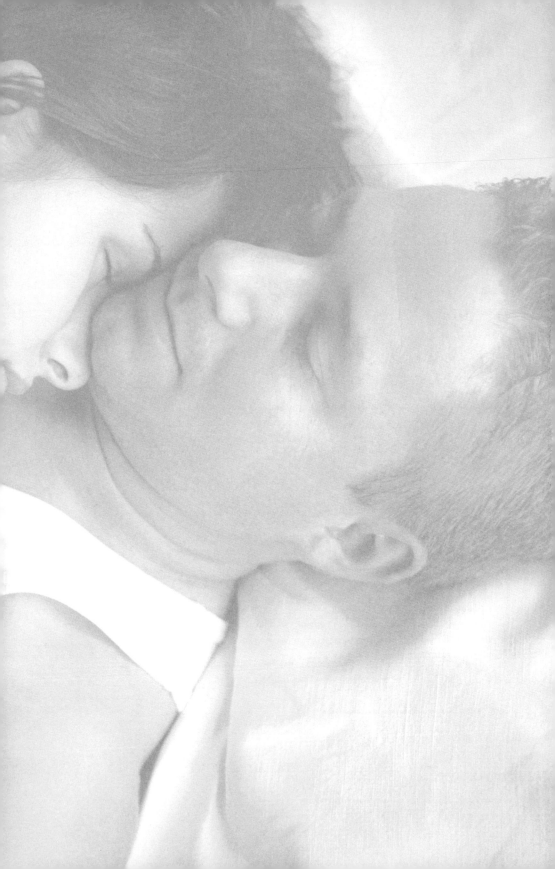

Last week we talked about "commitment" as the fuel of a great marriage. But being committed is just the start. During this session Chip will share 3 other keys that will build intimacy in your relationship. Consistently putting these keys into action in your marriage WILL break down walls and result in a more intimate relationship.

# TAKE IT IN

1. The "Fuel" of commitment – a lifelong choice of unconditional love to an imperfect person (covered in the previous session)

2. The "Oil" of _____ – A lifelong skill of learning to understand each other

▸   The Mandate – Ephesians 4:15-16

but speaking the truth in love, we are to grow up in all aspects into Him who is the head, even Christ, from whom the whole body, being fitted and held together by what every joint supplies, according to the proper working of each individual part, causes the growth of the body for the building up of itself in love.

— *Ephesians 4:15-16 (NASB)*

▸   The Rationale – To Know

▸   The How – A Weekly Conference

"The people whom I formed for Myself will declare My praise. Yet you have not called on Me, O Jacob; But you have become weary of Me, O Israel. "You have not brought to Me the sheep of your burnt offerings, Nor have you honored Me with your sacrifices. I have not burdened you with offerings, Nor wearied you with incense.

"You have bought Me not sweet cane with money, Nor have you filled Me with the fat of your sacrifices; Rather you have burdened Me with your sins, You have wearied Me with your iniquities. "I, even I, am the one who wipes out your transgressions for My own sake,

And I will not remember your sins. "Put Me in remembrance, let us argue our case together; State your cause, that you may be proved right.

— *Isaiah 43:21-26 (NASB)*

The people that you love the most can wound you the most deeply.

3. The "Tune-up" of _____ – an adventure of lifelong friendship, fun, and mutual fulfillment

- ► The Mandate – Genesis 2:18

- ► The Rationale – To Share

- ► The How – A Weekly Date

Take the initiative and make a plan.

> **Fun covers a multitude of sins.**

4. The "Navigational System" of _____ – a vision to impact the lives of others for Christ

The byproduct of serving together is relationally bonding.

- ► The Mandate – Matthew 28:19-20

- ► The Rationale – To serve

- ► The How – A Weekly Ministry

Personal Time + Supportive Friends +Renewing Activities = A "fully alive" you and a full battery to be a giver.

TALK IT OVER

1.   What's been most helpful so far that has come out of this series?

2.   Chip said that the "oil of communication" is a lifelong skill of learning to understand your mate. What is a new insight you have learned about your spouse in the last couple of years?

3.   How are you doing with maintaining some friendships and recreational activities (apart from your spouse) that are life-giving?

4.   Share an activity that you and your spouse enjoy doing together that is life-giving to your marriage.

5.   How have you been doing at keeping the spark of fun and adventure in your marriage? What could you do in the next month that would be a fun "tune-up" for you as a couple?

6.   Describe a meaningful experience when you and your spouse served together in ministry. Where could you see you and your spouse serving together in ministry on a regular basis?

LIVE IT OUT

Individually set aside some time this week to work on a personal game plan for developing your marriage. This could include a weekly date, a book you will read together, a ministry you will do together, or setting a time for your weekly conference. Give some intentional focus to your marriage. Then, go on a date and share your thoughts.

CONFLICT RESOLUTION
HOW TO FIGHT FAIR IN YOUR MARRIAGE

PART ONE

Conflict is inevitable. Every time you bring two people together, there will be conflict. The question is NOT "how do we have a conflict-free marriage?" The question is "how do we deal with the conflict that WILL come?" During this session Chip will help us to see how conflict can actually be a catalyst for intimacy.

 TAKE IT IN

Conflict is normal, biblical, and a key to growth.

We have to get over this naïve and unbiblical notion that conflict is wrong and abnormal.

CONFLICT RESOLUTION

- ▸ Conflict is normal.

- ▸ Conflict is an opportunity for growth.

- ▸ Conflict must be defused or it will destroy.

- ▸ Healthy conflict demands rules so no one gets hurt.

GOD'S PERSPECTIVE ON CONFLICT

Conflict is _____ in a fallen world.

"I have told you these things, so that in me you may have peace. In this world you will have trouble. But take heart! I have overcome the world."

— *John 16:33 (NIV)*

Conflict flows from our differences and our _____ .

- ▸ Differences in belief produce conflict. (Acts 15:1-35)

- ▸ Differences in perspective produce conflict. (Acts 15:36-41)

- ▸ Differences in style produce conflict. (Philippians 4:2-3)

- ▸ Selfish desires produce conflict. (James 4:1-3)

What causes fights and quarrels among you? Don't they come from your desires that battle within you? You want something but don't get it. You kill and covet, but you cannot have what you want. You quarrel and fight. You do not have, because you do not ask God. When you ask, you do not receive, because you ask with wrong motives, that you may spend what you get on your pleasures.

— James 4:1-3 (NIV)

Conflict Is an Opportunity for Growth (Philippians 2:1-4)

Therefore if there is any encouragement in Christ, if there is any consolation of love, if there is any fellowship of the Spirit, if any affection and compassion, make my joy complete by being of the same mind, maintaining the same love, united in spirit, intent on one purpose. Do nothing from selfishness or empty conceit, but with humility of mind regard one another as more important than yourselves; do not merely look out for your own personal interests, but also for the interests of others. Have this attitude in yourselves which was also in Christ Jesus,

— Philippians 2:1-5 (NASB)

In Christ, differences complement vs. _____ .
(Philippians 2:1-2)

In Christ, selfishness is transformed to
_____ .
(Philippians 2:3-4)

> **Humility in marriage =
> How can I serve you?**

In Christ, we can _____ and safely.
(Ephesians 4:25-32)

))) TALK IT OVER

1. When you were growing up, how was conflict handled in your family?

2. In what ways have you and your spouse gotten better about resolving conflict?

3. Ephesians 4:26-27 (NLT) says And *"don't sin by letting anger gain control over you." Don't let the sun go down while you are still angry, for anger gives a mighty foothold to the Devil.* How successful are you at NOT letting the sun go down while you are still angry? How successful are you and your spouse at actually resolving conflict?

4. Have someone in the group read aloud Philippians 2:6-8. From this passage, what can we learn from Jesus' example that can help us in our marriage?

    Who, being in very nature God, did not consider equality with God something to be grasped, but made himself nothing, taking the very nature of a servant, being made in human likeness. And being found in appearance as a man, he humbled himself and became obedient to death-- even death on a cross!

    — *Philippians 2:6-8 (NIV)*

5. At the end of this week's session, Chip talked about fighting "fair". As a group, brainstorm about a few "ground rules" for fighting fairly.

LIVE IT OUT

Set aside some time this week to have a conversation about "turtles" and "sharks". What are your tendencies? Establish some ground rules for your marriage and how you handle conflict. Is there currently any unresolved conflict that is simmering in your marriage?

If you are facing some serious conflict that you just can't seem to get past, consider seeking out some good Christian counseling.

Consider memorizing the following verse together as a couple. Talk about it and meditate on it. Have a discussion based on the last part of the verse. What are (selfish) desires within you that cause conflict in your marriage?

What causes fights and quarrels among you? Don't they come from your desires that battle within you?

— James 4:1 (NIV)

CONFLICT RESOLUTION
HOW TO FIGHT FAIR IN YOUR MARRIAGE

PART TWO

In the last session we began discussing conflict and how conflict is a natural part of every relationship. We all know how to have a "fight" but many of us don't know how to "fight fair". And, we often don't know how to diffuse conflict. In this session, Chip is going to provide us some very practical tools that we can start using this week to help us with conflict in our marriage.

 TAKE IT IN

The person God is going to use most to help your mate be like Jesus is YOU.

The most common communication styles can be likened to sharks or turtles.

TURTLES – THE GOAL IS TO "AVOID"

- ▸ Can clam up and not speak
- ▸ Can give you the cold shoulder
- ▸ Can withdraw affection
- ▸ Can avoid and redirect
- ▸ Can run to diversionary interests (alcohol, spending, pleasure)
- ▸ Natural inclination is to "withdraw"

SHARKS – THE GOAL IS TO "WIN"

- ▸ Can try to be mind readers
- ▸ Can do blame shifting
- ▸ Can keep score
- ▸ Can use logic to escape emotional reality
- ▸ Can use big threats or humiliation
- ▸ Natural inclination is to "attack"

HOW TO DIFFUSE CONFLICT IN YOUR MARRIAGE

D – _____ **the problem (on your own). (Proverbs 15:14)**

Questions to ask yourself…

- ▶ What's bothering me?

- ▶ When did this begin?

- ▶ What is it that I am feeling?

Learn to separate the problem from the person.

I – _____ **a time to talk. (Matthew 5:23-24)**

The discerning heart seeks knowledge, but the mouth of a fool feeds on folly.

— *Proverbs 15:14 (NIV)*

F – _____ **on the perceived problem, not the person. (Proverbs 18:19)**

An offended brother is more unyielding than a fortified city, and disputes are like the barred gates of a citadel.

— *Proverbs 18:19 (NIV)*

F – _____ **their pain as though it were your own. (Proverbs 17:17)**

A friend loves at all times, and a brother is born for adversity.

— *Proverbs 17:17 (NIV)*

> Your "will" is the engine of life and "feelings" are the caboose.

U – _____ **the root problem. (Proverbs 20:5)**

SYMPTOM	ROOT
▶ MONEY	▶ VALUES, PRIORITIES, POWER/CONTROL ISSUES
▶ SEX	▶ COMMUNICATION, UNMET EMOTIONAL NEEDS, PAST HISTORY/BAGGAGE
▶ IN-LAWS	▶ LOYALTY, EXPECTATIONS
▶ CHILDREN/WORK	▶ ROLES AND/OR GOALS

S – _____ **things right between you. (James 5:16)**

Therefore confess your sins to each other and pray for each other so that you may be healed.

— James 5:16a (NIV)

> ► Own your responsibility.
>
> ► Confess – "I was wrong…"
>
> ► Ask forgiveness – "Will you forgive me?"

E – _____ **a specific action plan that addresses the issue discussed – write it down. (James 1:22-25)**

> ► Husband – I commit to… by (when?)
>
> ► Wife – I commit to… by (when?)

Do not merely listen to the word, and so deceive yourselves. Do what it says. Anyone who listens to the word but does not do what it says is like a man who looks at his face in a mirror and, after looking at himself, goes away and immediately forgets what he looks like. But the man who looks intently into the perfect law that gives freedom, and continues to do this, not forgetting what he has heard, but doing it--he will be blessed in what he does.

— James 1:22-25 (NIV)

 TALK IT OVER

1. Go around the room and one by one share whether you are a turtle or shark. Then, briefly explain why you see yourself that way.

2. Based on the tendencies (shark or turtle) of both you and your spouse, what do you need to be careful about when it comes to conflict?

3. Which one of the 7 DIFFUSE principles do you personally need to work on the most?

4. Complete the following statement (to your spouse). "For us to handle conflict effectively, you need to understand that I…"

5. What are the one or two most common issues that end up being a conflict? Can you put your finger on anything that might be a root issue behind the conflict?

 LIVE IT OUT

Sometime this week, go through the DIFFUSE process yourself. Then, set a time with your spouse to go through this process together. If this is the first time you have done something like this with your spouse, be sensitive. Go slow and easy, with lots of love and prayer.

MEN & WOMEN
ENJOYING THE
DIFFERENCE

PART ONE

One of the most delicate and touchy topics in our culture is the discussion regarding gender roles. The Bible has a lot to say about the role of women and men in marriage. But, there has been a lot of misunderstanding about these issues that has caused unnecessary stress and tension. During this session, Chip will provide straightforward, insightful, and Biblical teaching. When we can learn to embrace our God-given roles, the "dance" of marriage will be a lot more graceful.

⬤ TALK IT OVER

Is your marriage
a "dance" or a "debate"?

A GREAT DANCE DEMANDS...

- ► A Choreographer

- ► Mutual Submission to His "Steps"

- ► Clarity of Roles

- ► Practice, Practice, and More Practice

A GREAT DANCE DEVELOPS...

- ► An Incredible Team

- ► Balance, Timing, Rhythm, and Strength

- ► Personal Joy and Joint Fulfillment

- ► A Thing of Beauty

GOD'S DESIGN FOR "THE DANCE" OF MARRIAGE

> In the dance of marriage, God is the choreographer.

There must be submission to the choreographer.

Submit to one another out of reverence for Christ.
— Ephesians 5:21 (NIV)

The starting place for a great marriage dance is mutual submission and dying to your own selfish desires.

A WORD TO WOMEN – FOLLOW HIS _____

Wives, submit to your husbands as to the Lord. For the husband is the head of the wife as Christ is the head of the church, his body, of which he is the Savior. Now as the church submits to Christ, so also wives should submit to their husbands in everything.
— Ephesians 5:22-24 (NIV)

WHO IS LEADING "THE DANCE"?

- ▸ Who handles the money?
- ▸ Who disciplines the children?
- ▸ Who initiates discussion of future plans or problems?
- ▸ Who asks the most questions and who makes the most statements?

FOLLOWING YOUR HUSBAND'S LEAD

- ▸ The Command – Be subject to your husband.
- ▸ The Reason – The husband is the head.

Now I want you to realize that the head of every man is Christ, and the head of the woman is man, and the head of Christ is God.
— 1 Corinthians 11:3 (NIV)

WHAT DOES THIS MEAN? –

▸   Marriage is not a 50/50 proposition.

▸   There are specific roles and functions and lines of authority in marriage.

▸   These roles flow out of God's sovereign design and our mutual submission to one another.

▸   The woman voluntarily submits out of love to her husband.

▸   A woman's greatest fulfillment and joy will be achieved and embraced by following God's design.

 TALK IT OVER

For this week's discussion time let the women and men meet separately.

1.   **WOMEN** – In what ways has the culture made it difficult for you to follow your husband's lead?
     MEN – In what specific ways are you making it hard for your wife to follow?

2.   How would you define the different roles your parents played in their marriage? What was their marriage dance like?

3. Paul said in Ephesians 5:21 Submit to one another out of reverence for Christ. What would this mean practically in your relationship with your spouse? Be specific.

4. **WOMEN** – How are you doing at following your husband's lead?
   MEN – What positive steps can you take that will help your wife want to follow your lead?

5. **WOMEN** – What one action step are you willing to commit to this week to better follow your husband's lead? Share this with the other women and then pray for each other and check in with each other this coming week.
   MEN – What one action step are you willing to commit to this week to love and serve your wife better? Share this with the other men and then pray for each other and check in with each other this week.

 LIVE IT OUT

Set aside some time this week to discuss with your spouse your specific roles within your marriage. Spend some time sharing how your parents did the marriage "dance" and how their roles were defined. Also, it might be helpful to review the discussion questions from this week when you met separately as men and women.

MEN & WOMEN
ENJOYING THE
DIFFERENCE

PART TWO

Welcome to our final session in this study. Thanks for your perseverance and faithfulness in completing this marriage series. During this final session Chip will help husbands to understand what it looks like to be a godly leader worth following. May God pour out his richest blessings on your marriage and may your marriage be a shining reflection of the love relationship between Christ and his bride, the church.

 TAKE IT IN

God's Design for "The Dance" of Marriage – Ephesians 5:21-33

A WORD TO MEN – BE WORTHY OF FOLLOWING.

> *Husbands, love your wives, just as Christ loved the church and gave himself up for her to make her holy, cleansing her by the washing with water through the word, and to present her to himself as a radiant church, without stain or wrinkle or any other blemish, but holy and blameless.*
>
> *In this same way, husbands ought to love their wives as their own bodies. He who loves his wife loves himself. After all, no one ever hated his own body, but he feeds and cares for it, just as Christ does the church-- for we are members of his body.*
>
> — *Ephesians 5:25-30 (NIV)*

Men, we are to make it our goal to love our wives with the same reckless sacrifice and abandonment that Jesus had in dying for his church.

The Command – Love your wives as Christ loved the church.

The Purpose – Help your wife to reach her full potential.

Be as intentional with
your marriage as
you are your job.

WHAT DOES THIS MEAN?	WHAT DOES THIS NOT MEAN?
► Husbands must love sacrificially.	► That you always give in to what your wife wants
► Husbands must love with intentionality.	► That you don't have a life outside your marriage
► Husbands must love sensitively.	► That you smother your wife or make her totally dependent on you

A WORD TO THE WORLD – IT'S ABOUT WHAT _____ WANTS TO DO THROUGH THE DANCE.

"For this reason a man will leave his father and mother and be united to his wife, and the two will become one flesh." This is a profound mystery--but I am talking about Christ and the church. However, each one of you also must love his wife as he loves himself, and the wife must respect her husband.

— *Ephesians 5:31-33 (NIV)*

The dance should point people to the choreographer.

))) TALK IT OVER

1. Think of a couple that you know that you think is a great example of God's design for marriage. Share their name and what you have observed in their marriage that makes it a great dance.

2.   Ladies, complete the following statement (to your husband) "You could help me reach my full potential by ..."

3.   Paul said that our marriages are to be a picture of the relationship between Christ and His bride the Church. Your marriage was meant to point others to God. Whose marriage could you impact and influence? What tangible thing could you do to invest in their marriage?

4.   What is your big "take away" from this series? How will that impact you and your marriage going forward?

5.   Close out this series with a time of affirmation and celebration. Share with others in the group how you have seen God at work in them. Affirm the growth and changes and effort that people have put into their marriage.

LIVE IT OUT

Let this be the beginning, not the end. Commit to investing in your marriage from this day forward. Consider finding a marriage enrichment event to attend or read a marriage book together with your spouse. Regularly go back and review the principles and tools from this series. It is so easy to slip back into old patterns and habits, but with diligence and with God's help, your best years can be ahead. Enjoy the dance.

LEADER'S NOTES

THE FOLLOWING RESOURCES ARE VALUABLE
TO HELP YOU EFFECTIVELY LEAD AND
FACILITATE YOUR GROUP:

- ► GROUP AGREEMENT

- ► GUIDELINES: HOW TO MAKE THIS
  A MEANINGFUL EXPERIENCE FOR
  YOUR GROUP

- ► SESSION NOTES

- ► PRAYER & PRAISE

- ► GROUP ROSTER

GROUP AGREEMENT

People come to groups with a variety of different expectations. The purpose of a group agreement is simply to make sure everyone is on the same page and that we have some common expectations.

The following Group Agreement is a tool to help you discuss specific guidelines during your first meeting. Modify anything that does not work for your group, then be sure to discuss the questions in the section called Our Game Plan. This will help you to have an even greater group experience!

WE AGREE TO THE FOLLOWING PRIORITIES

Take the Bible Seriously	To seek to understand and apply God's truth in the Bible
Group Attendance	To give priority to the group meeting (call if I am going to be absent or late)
Safe Environment	To create a safe place where people can be heard and feel loved (no snap judgments or simple fixes)
Respectful Discussion	To speak in a respectful and honoring way to our mate and others in the group
Be Confidential	To keep anything that is shared strictly confidential and within the group
Spiritual Health	To give group members permission to help me live a godly, healthy spiritual life that is pleasing to God
Building Relationships	To get to know the other members of the group and pray for them regularly
Prayer	To regularly pray with and for each other
Other	_____
	_____
	_____
	_____

OUR GAME PLAN

▶   Will we have refreshments? _____

▶   What will we do about childcare? _____

▶   What day and time will we meet? _____

▶   Where will we meet? _____

▶   How long will we meet each week? _____

HOW TO MAKE THIS A MEANINGFUL EXPERIENCE FOR YOUR GROUP

BEFORE THE GROUP ARRIVES

1. **BE PREPARED.** Your personal preparation can make a huge difference in the quality of the group experience. We strongly suggest previewing both the DVD teaching by Chip Ingram and the study guide.

2. **PRAY FOR YOUR GROUP MEMBERS BY NAME.** Ask God to use your time together to touch the heart of every person in your group. Expect God to challenge and change people as a result of this study.

3. **PROVIDE REFRESHMENTS.** There's nothing like food to help a group relax and connect with each other. For the first week, we suggest you prepare a snack, but after that, ask other group members to bring the food so that they share in the responsibilities of the group and make a commitment to return.

4. **RELAX.** Don't try to imitate someone else's style of leading a group. Lead the group in a way that fits your style and temperament. Remember that people may feel nervous showing up for a small group study, so put them at ease when they arrive. Make sure to have all the details covered prior to your group meeting, so that once people start arriving, you can focus on them.

 ## TAKE IT IN (WATCH THE VIDEO)

1. **GET THE VIDEO READY.** Each video session on the DVD will have 3 components. The first 2-3 minutes Chip will introduce this week's topic Then, you will watch the actual teaching content that Chip taught in front of a live audience. This portion of the video will be roughly 20 minutes in length. Finally, Chip will then share some closing thoughts and set up the discussion time for your group.

2. **TEST THE EQUIPMENT.** The video segments flow from one right into the next. So, once you start the session, you won't have to stop the video until Chip has finished his closing thoughts and prepared the group for the first discussion question. Be sure to test your video equipment ahead of time and make sure you have located this week's lesson on the DVD menu.

3. **HAVE AMPLE MATERIALS.** Before you start the video, also make sure everyone has their own copy of the study guide. Encourage the group to open to this week's session and follow along with the teaching. There is an outline in the study guide with an opportunity to fill in the outline.

4. **ARRANGE THE ROOM.** Set up the chairs in the room so that everyone can see the television. And, arrange the room in such a way that it is conducive to discussion.

TALK IT OVER

Here are some guidelines for leading the discussion time:

1. **MAKE THIS A DISCUSSION, NOT A LECTURE.** Resist the temptation to do all the talking, and to answer your own questions. Don't be afraid of a few moments of silence while people formulate their answers. And don't feel like you need to have all the answers. There is nothing wrong with simply responding "I don't know the answer to that, but I'll see if I can find an answer this week".

2. **ENCOURAGE EVERYONE TO PARTICIPATE.** Don't let one person dominate, but also don't pressure quieter members to speak during the first couple of sessions. Because this is a marriage series, it may be hard for some people to open up and be honest. Be patient. Ask good follow up questions and be sensitive to delicate issues.

3. **AFFIRM PEOPLE'S PARTICIPATION AND INPUT.** If an answer is clearly wrong, ask "What led you to that conclusion?" or ask what the rest of the group thinks. If a disagreement arises, don't be too quick to shut it down! The discussion can draw out important perspectives, and if you can't resolve it there, offer to research it further and return to the issue next week.However, if someone goes on the offensive and engages in personal attack of their spouse, you will need to step in as the leader. In the midst of spirited discussion, we must also remember that people are fragile and there is no place for disrespect.

4. **DETOUR WHEN NECESSARY.** If an important question is raised that is not in the study guide, take time to discuss it. Also, if someone shares something personal and emotional, take time for them. Stop and pray for them right then. Allow the Holy Spirit room to maneuver, and follow his prompting when the discussion changes direction.

5. **SUBGROUP.** One of the principles of small group life is "when numbers go up, sharing goes down". So, if you have a large group, sometimes you may want to split up into groups of 4-6 for the discussion time. This is a great way to give everyone, even the quieter members, a chance to say something. Choose someone in the group to guide each of the smaller groups through the discussion. This involves others in the leadership of the group, and provides an opportunity for training new leaders.

6. **PRAYER.** Be sensitive to the fact that some people in your group may be uncomfortable praying out loud. As a general rule, don't call on people to pray unless you have asked them ahead of time or have heard them pray in public. But this can also be a time to help people build their confidence to pray in a group. Consider having prayer times that ask people to just say a word or sentence of thanks to God.

 ## LIVE IT OUT

These simple suggestions will help couples apply the lesson. Be sure and leave adequate time to talk about these practical applications of the lesson. Most of the weekly assignments involve setting aside time as a couple to talk about specific marriage issues raised that week during the session. Encourage the couples to make this a priority and check in with others to see if people are following through. Then occasionally ask people if they want to share anything from their discussion that week.

SESSION NOTES

SESSION 1
God's Dream for Your Marriage
PART ONE

▸ Once people start arriving, focus on the people and not the logistics. Try to make everyone feel welcome and comfortable. Be sure to take a few moments for people to introduce themselves and get acquainted.

▸ Go over the group agreement and game plan. Also, review the *How to Get the Most Out of This Experience* section at the front of their study guide. Do this prior to watching the video teaching.

▸ As a way to introduce the whole series, you might want to read to the group the page entitled "A Word from Chip".

▸ Be sensitive to the fact that being in a small group might be a new experience for some. And, participating in a marriage study can be unnerving for some. So, let people engage and participate at a pace that is comfortable for them. Be cautious about calling on people to answer questions, read a scripture passage or pray in front of the group.

SESSION 2
God's Dream for Your Marriage
PART TWO

▸ As you start this week's session, you may want to follow up from last week's assignment. People were to set aside some time to reminisce and discuss the early days of their relationship. It might be fun during each session to have a couple share a little of their story... how they met, how they got engaged and a little about their wedding.

▸ During this week's session, the group will be taking an Intimacy Assessment, looking at spiritual, emotional, and physical intimacy. Be sure to have some extra pens on hand for people to fill out the assessment.

▸ One of the areas Chip will talk about this week is Spiritual Intimacy. This is a weak area for most couples. So, you might want to suggest that couples try praying together this next week.

▸ For your discussion time this week, Chip is going to suggest sub-grouping. He suggests putting 2 couples together for the discussion time. When discussion groups are smaller, there is more time for individuals to share. Also, people will often be more transparent in a smaller group.

What Went Wrong — Barriers to Intimacy

PART ONE

▸ If there is anyone or any couple that missed last week's session, make sure to contact them and let them know they were missed.

▸ Now that the group has been going a couple of weeks, this might be a good time to enlist some help from others. The more people are involved, the more ownership they will have of the group. So, get someone to help with refreshments, someone to keep up with prayer requests, and someone to plan a group social.

▸ At the end of this week's session you will find an assignment for memorizing Scripture. Most Christians struggle with this discipline and yet it is a powerful tool for our spiritual growth. Couples will be encouraged to memorize Romans 12:10 together. Encourage couples to try this together. It is a simple and short verse that every couple could memorize.

▸ One of the greatest gifts you give those you lead is your personal care and prayer on their behalf. Before you go into your meeting this week, spend a few moments praying for each couple in your group. Based on what you have observed or discerned, pray specifically for these couples.

What Went Wrong — Barriers to Intimacy

PART TWO

▸ As you get ready for your group meeting this week, think for a moment about the last 3 meetings. How has the discussion been? Has it been engaging? Has it been negative? Is there any couple who seems to not be participating? Or is there a couple who is dominating? Do your best to get everyone participating. A good facilitator draws people out without making them feel singled out.

▸ As the study progresses, hopefully the level of openness and honesty will increase. Now that we are in session 4 and people are getting to know one another, they should feel more comfortable sharing honestly with the group. One of the best ways to facilitate deeper honesty is for you to model this as the group leader. If you will lead and be vulnerable and transparent, others will feel permission to do the same.

▸ As the end of this week's session, Chip will explain the gospel and offer the opportunity for people to come to Christ. He will encourage them to go to you as the leader. So, if you know of any in the group who aren't believers, please pray that they will be open to the gospel this week. Also, be ready to help them on their journey to salvation.

SESSION 5

How to Share Hearts Instead of Exchange Words

PART ONE

▸ This week's session is all about communication. This is a major issue and struggle for many couples. Make sure that as the group gets more honest in their discussion that the sharing is appropriate. If someone is being negative or accusatory or attacking their mate, you might need to step in and redirect the discussion.

▸ Pay special attention this week to Chip as he talks about the different levels of communication. One of the discussion questions this week is a follow up to the 5 levels of communication. It would be helpful for you to look over the discussion questions this week ahead of time.

▸ One of the best ways to strengthen the sense of community and friendship within the group is to do something apart from the group meeting. Consider planning a social or dinner at a restaurant with all the couples.

SESSION 6

How to Share Hearts Instead of Exchange Words

PART TWO

▸ This week Chip is going to introduce some very practical tools that can help all of us in our marriages. One of the tools he will introduce will be The Marriage Conference. At the end of the session he will encourage the group to break up into couples and for the couples to sit facing each other. Then, they will spend a few minutes asking each other a set of 3 questions. The questions are listed in the study guide. Be sure to give couples adequate time for this exercise. After everyone is done, bring the group back together for the rest of the discussion.

▸ In order to make sure that we don't interrupt our spouse, Chip playfully suggests putting duct tape over our mouth. To make this more fun, you may want to get a roll of duct tape to have available for couples.

▸ In the Live It Out section, couples will be encouraged to memorize another verse together. You might want to have little 3x5 cards available for people to write out the verse. Encourage them to take this seriously and to work on memorizing the verse as a couple.

▸ We are now at the halfway point in this series. Affirm the group for their commitment and faithfulness. Also remind them that we are just getting started. But, as they work on their marriages and put these tools to use, they can improve their relationship with their spouse.

LEADER'S NOTES

SESSION 7
The Four Keys to Intimacy
PART ONE

▸ This week Chip will encourage you as the facilitator to lead off the discussion. You modeling openness and transparency will give others the courage to do the same.

▸ Much of this week's session is about God's desire for us to make a lifelong commitment to our spouse. It is likely that someone in your group has been through divorce. Be sensitive to this reality. Don't do anything that would shame or humiliate them about their past. Focus on the importance of a lifelong commitment going forward.

▸ One of the assignments this week is to write a love letter to your spouse declaring your lifelong commitment to them. Talk about this challenge with the group and especially challenge the men to step up to the plate, give this some focus and creativity. You might want to send out an e-mail this week as a reminder and also see if anyone is willing to share their letter with the group.

SESSION 8
The Four Keys to Intimacy
PART TWO

▸ As your group begins to develop friendships with each other, it would be good to stress critical components that encourage authentic relationships. The first is confidentiality. Stress the importance of this being a "safe place" where people can share without worrying if it will get outside the group. The second component is time together outside the group meeting. If the group really wants to go to a deeper level, they will need to start developing their friendships beyond the small group meeting.

▸ During this session, Chip is going to talk about romance and keeping the spark in your marriage. The truth is that most couples fall into a rut and the romance wanes. Chip is going to suggest a weekend getaway. You might want to consider challenging the group to do this within the next month. Do some brainstorming about places to go and things to do. Then, hold each other accountable for a romantic getaway.

▸ Last week the couples were encouraged to write a love letter declaring their lifelong commitment to each other. See if there is someone in the group who would be willing to share their letter or at least talk about what getting that letter meant to them.

SESSION 9
Conflict Resolution – How to Fight Fair in Your Marriage
PART ONE

► This week's topic is a delicate one. It is all about conflict and how we resolve it. You will want to be especially sensitive to the discussion this week to make sure that the conversation is appropriate and constructive. You might even want to set up the discussion time with the challenge to keep it positive and constructive.

► One of the best ways to build authentic community in your group is to pray for and with each other. Too often prayer is simply tacked on to the end of our group meeting when everyone is ready to get home. Talk to your group about praying for each other and this week try to make the prayer time a meaningful part of the group experience. Get a little creative with the prayer time so your group doesn't get in a rut.

► As you think about your group, is there someone else who might be a good group facilitator? As a way to help develop other leaders you might want to consider having someone else lead next week's study or at least having them lead a portion of the study. Giving people responsibility helps them to grow in their own walk with the Lord.

SESSION 10
Conflict Resolution – How to Fight Fair in Your Marriage
PART TWO

► When people begin to share very personally about their marriage, our tendency is to try to fix their problem or offer advice. Many of the conflicts in marriages are complicated and are not easily resolved. The best response from your group is to offer support and prayer rather than quick fixes. You may also want to stress confidentiality.

► Question 5 in your discussion time this week has the potential to surface some issues that are a constant battle with their mate. So, don't pressure anyone to share that isn't ready to do so. If someone does share about their struggle with conflict in their marriage, follow up with them this week. Let them know you are praying for them and that you are available if they need a sympathetic ear.

► If it is obvious that one of the couples is having serious conflict issues that they just can't seem to get past, you might want to find the name of a good Christian counselor in your area that you might recommend to them.

► Since there are only 2 more sessions after this one, you should start talking about what your group will do next. Are you going to do another study? If so, you might consider some of the curriculum available from www.LivingontheEdge.org.

LEADER'S NOTES

SESSION 11
Men & Women –
Enjoying the Difference
PART ONE

▸ This week's topic is about the roles of men and women in marriage. As you know, this is a touchy and sensitive topic in our culture. Chip does a wonderful job of handling this topic and he will challenge the group to not let this topic become a point of debate. He will speak more to the women this week but will focus on the men in the next session.

▸ For the discussion time, Chip will ask for the men and women to meet separately. And, in the study guide this week you will find a set of questions for men and a set of discussion questions for women.

▸ Since this is the next to last session, don't forget to talk about what your group is going to do after this study is over.

▸ Since this study is drawing to a close, consider planning some kind of social or party for the group. After you have completed the final session, it is a good idea to plan a social/party for the following week. Have some great food and let people share how God has used this series in their marriages. Make it a casual and informal time to laugh, share, and celebrate what God has done.

SESSION 12
Men & Women –
Enjoying the Difference
PART TWO

▸ This week's topic will focus specifically on the role of men in marriage. At the end of the video Chip will warn us not to focus on our spouse's role and the verses that apply to them. He will challenge us to focus on our role and the Scriptures that apply to me.

▸ The final discussion question this week will encourage you to have a time of affirmation and celebration. Have people share with other couples in the group how they have seen God at work in them. Affirm the growth and changes and effort that people have put into their marriage. It might be helpful for you to lead out in this little exercise.

▸ It has been our prayer that this would be a rich, fruitful experience for your group. As you close this last meeting in this study, consider having a brief prayer time that simply expresses gratitude to God for what he has done in the lives of your group.

▸ From those of us at Living on the Edge, we want to say "thanks" for leading the group through this series. We are grateful that you made yourself available. May God bless you for your faithfulness.

PRAYER & PRAISE

One of the most important things you can do in your group is to pray with and for each other. Write down each other's concerns here so you can remember to pray for these requests during the week!

Use the Follow Up box to record an answer to prayer or to write down how you might want to follow up with the person making the request. This could be a phone call, an e-mail or a card. Your personal concern will mean a lot!

PERSON	PRAYER REQUEST	FOLLOW UP

PRAYER & PRAISE

PERSON	PRAYER REQUEST	FOLLOW UP

PRAYER & PRAISE

PERSON	PRAYER REQUEST	FOLLOW UP

PRAYER & PRAISE

PERSON	PRAYER REQUEST	FOLLOW UP

PRAYER & PRAISE

PERSON	PRAYER REQUEST	FOLLOW UP

GROUP ROSTER

NAME	HOME PHONE	EMAIL

Small Group Studies offered by Chip Ingram.

GOD: AS HE LONGS FOR YOU TO SEE HIM

How would you describe God? Awesome? All Powerful? Creator? While we cannot know Him exhaustively, we can know Him truly. And God longs for you to see Him as He truly is. Join Chip in this fascinating series studying the seven attributes of God.

MIRACLE OF LIFE CHANGE

Is life change really possible? If we're honest most of us would answer, "No." You've tried numerous programs that promise big changes, but in reality, deliver very little results. You long for transformation, but don't know where to begin. There's good news for you and there is hope. Life change is possible!

LIVING ON THE EDGE (R12)

Being a genuine disciple of Christ flows out of a relationship with Him. It's about experiencing God's grace, not earning His love through performance. A real relationship with Jesus Christ will produce a follower whose life looks progressively more like His life.

INVISIBLE WAR

Beneath our tangible landscape lurks an invisible spiritual realm where an unseen battle rages. It's real and it's dangerous. If you're prepared to remove the blinders and gaze into the unseen world, Chip is ready to take you there.

EFFECTIVE PARENTING IN A DEFECTIVE WORLD

Raising children is a tough challenge in today's world. Peers and pop culture exert a never-ending pressure on kids. But the good news is that God has been working with people from bad situations for a long time! In Effective Parenting you will learn how God's principles for raising children still work today. Packed with practical advice, this series will give struggling parents a vision for their children's future and life-changing help for today!

EXPERIENCING GOD'S DREAM FOR YOUR MARRIAGE

Would you like a fresh breeze to blow in your marriage? Do you long for a marriage where intimacy and communication are a reality instead of a dream? "Experiencing God's Dream for Your Marriage" is a topical series by Chip Ingram examining God's design for marriage, with practical instruction to help you make your marriage what God desires it to be.

FIVE LIES THAT RUIN RELATIONSHIPS

Have you ever looked back over a situation or relationship in your life and wondered how it became so messy or difficult? In this study, we'll define five of the most common lies that have the potential to ruin relationships with those we love. What we think about life determines how we live it, so there is power in knowing and applying God's truth.

LOVE, SEX & LASTING RELATIONSHIPS

Everyone wants to love and be loved. The pursuit of "true love" is everywhere you look! It's romanticized on TV and in the movies we watch. There are books about it, songs about it, internet dating, and even seminars on it... all of which are designed to "help" you find that special someone to love. So why is "true love" so elusive? Could it be that the picture of love we see in today's culture is nothing more than an illusion?

BALANCING LIFE'S DEMANDS

Are you busy, tired, stressed out, and stretched to the limit? Does life seem a little out of control? Are you running long on "to do's" and short on time? If so, join us in this series, Balancing Life's Demands. You'll learn how to put "first things first" and find peace in the midst of pressure and adversity. No clichés or quick fixes, just practical biblical insights to help you order your personal world.

REBUILDING YOUR BROKEN WORLD

Lives today are filled with pain. Either through stress, pressure, unfortunate circumstances or bad decisions, many of us find ourselves living in a world that has fallen apart. This series from James 1 is designed to help you begin where you are and rebuild your broken world.

WHY I BELIEVE

An apologetic series to address your "honest doubts" and most pivotal questions about the claims of the Christian fatih – What Happens When We Die? Can Miracles Be Explained? Is There Really A God? Answers to questions such as these are as varied as they are confusing and spring from a plethora of mystical belief systems. But the fact is, we can know the truth. There are solid, logical answers to satisfy the heart and the mind of those who are seeking.